STAR WARS

ZAM WESELL

SPEEDER ZAM'S SPEEDER ZAM'S S

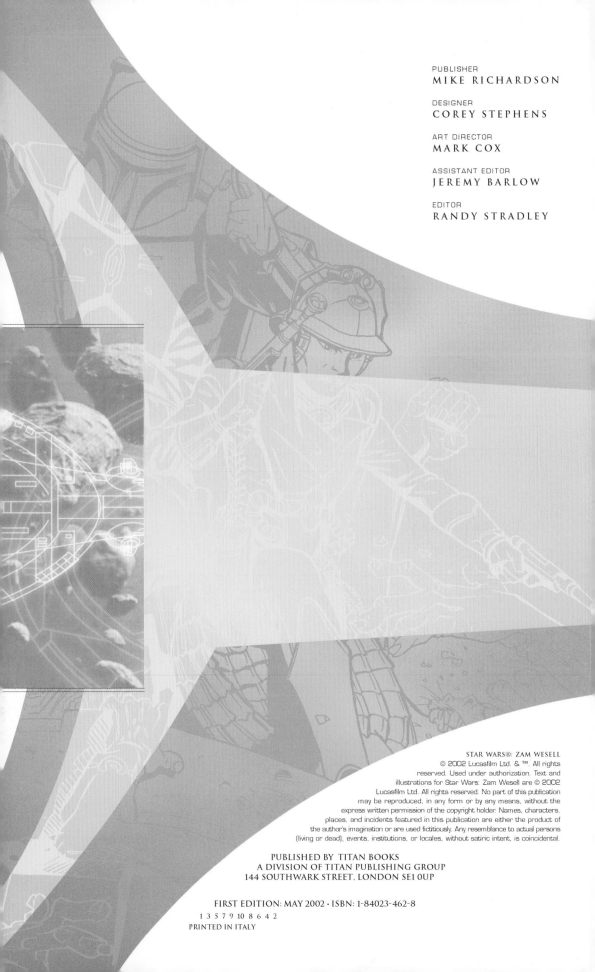

PUBLISHER
MIKE RICHARDSON

DESIGNER
COREY STEPHENS

ART DIRECTOR
MARK COX

ASSISTANT EDITOR
JEREMY BARLOW

EDITOR
RANDY STRADLEY

PUBLISHED BY TITAN BOOKS
A DIVISION OF TITAN PUBLISHING GROUP
144 SOUTHWARK STREET, LONDON SE1 0UP

FIRST EDITION: MAY 2002 · ISBN: 1-84023-462-8
1 3 5 7 9 10 8 6 4 2
PRINTED IN ITALY

STAR WARS®

ZAM WESELL

STORY BY	RON MARZ
ART BY	TED NAIFEH
COLORING BY	DAVE STEWART & DIGITAL CHAMELEON
LETTERING BY	DIGITAL CHAMELEON

...YOUR GRIEVANCES AGAINST THESE OVERLORDS WE MUST TOPPLE.

PERHAPS YOU SERVED WITH ME UPON ANNOO...

...OR YOU HAVE BEEN BRANDED OUTLAWS AND WRONGLY PURSUED...

...OR YOU HAVE LONG WANTED TO PUNISH THE REPUBLIC BUT LACKED THE MEANS.

WHATEVER YOUR MOTIVATIONS...

...YOU HOLD IN COMMON YOUR WILLINGNESS TO SACRIFICE YOURSELF FOR THE CAUSE.

WE WILL BE SWIFT.

WE WILL BE DEADLY.

WE WILL BE UNSTOPPABLE.

THIS SLIPPED FROM MY GRASP FOR A TIME. BUT ONCE AGAIN I HOLD THE INSTRUMENT OF OUR VENGEANCE...

...AND WITH IT WE WILL REDUCE CORUSCANT TO DUST!

IT CAN HAVE THE BRAT!

RUN!

...WHAT HAPPENED?

I BELIEVE THEY SAW SOMETHING THAT FRIGHTENED THEM...

WELL...

...IF YOU'RE JEDI, WHAT ARE YOU DOING DOWN HERE? PEOPLE LIKE YOU DON'T USUALLY COME DOWN HERE. NOT IF THEY DON'T HAVE TO.

I'M LOOKING FOR SOMETHING.

SOMETHING YOU LOST?

NO, SOMETHING SOMEONE ELSE POSSESSES. A BAD THING.

I DON'T WANT THEM TO USE IT TO HURT ANYONE, SO I HAVE TO FIND IT AND TAKE IT AWAY.

Oh.

HOW WILL YOU FIND IT?

I CAN FEEL IT. I CAN REACH OUT AND FEEL IT WITH MY MIND, A BIT LIKE THAT TRICK WITH THE GANG... THE WAY YOU CAN TELL IF A LAMP IS ON EVEN WHEN YOUR EYES ARE CLOSED.

I THINK I'M GETTING CLOSE, BUT IT'S DEEPER. THAT WAY, I THINK.

I SHOULD BE GOING. AND YOU SHOULD HURRY HOME.

WILL YOU BE ALL RIGHT?

YEAH, I DON'T THINK SPIZ IS GOING TO BOTHER ME FOR QUITE A WHILE.

THANKS FOR SAVING ME.

I HOPE YOU FIND WHAT YOU'RE LOOKING FOR!

SO DO I.

AAAAH!

THE GREAT JANGO FETT-- REDUCED TO SCARING A BUNCH OF TEENAGE HOOLIGANS.

SUCH A SHAME TO SEE A BOUNTY HUNTER WHO'S LOST HIS EDGE.

WHAT DID YOU LEARN?

I LEARNED THE FOOD AT THE *TWIRLING TWI'LEK* STINKS.

I *ALSO* LEARNED NOBODY'S TALKING VERY MUCH...

...NOT EVEN TO A *DUG* NAMED *FERNOODA* WHO'S KNOWN TO HAVE CLOSE TIES TO GENERAL KHORDA.

BUT TONGUES TEND TO LOOSEN AFTER YOU BUY ENOUGH *DRINKS*.

KHORDA HIMSELF HASN'T BEEN SEEN, BUT A HALF-DOZEN OF HIS ASSOCIATES ARE *DEFINITELY* HERE.

IT'S A SAFE BET KHORDA'S HERE AS WELL. HE'S JUST BEEN MORE CAREFUL ABOUT ANNOUNCING IT.

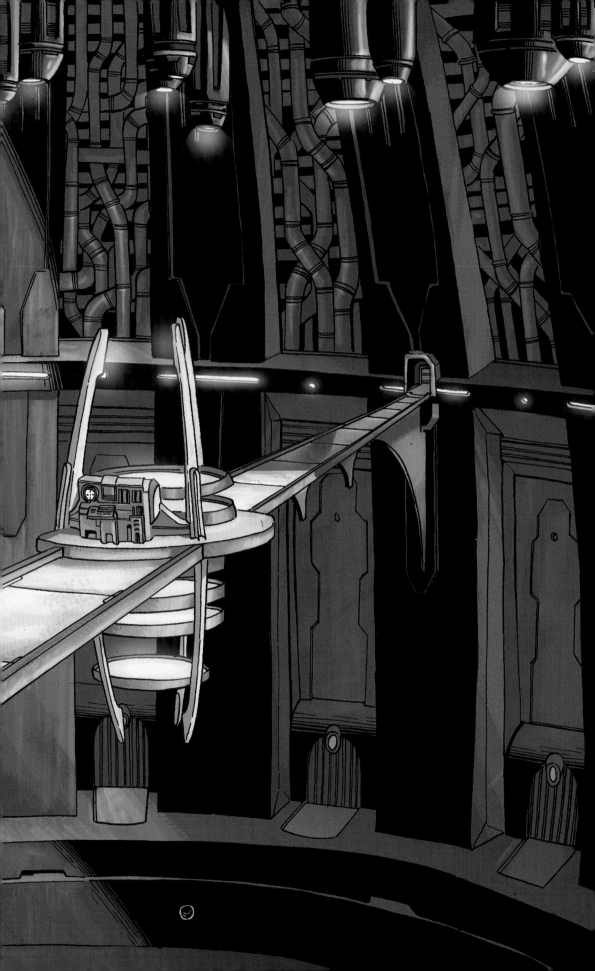

...WE HAVE COMPANY.

EASY... IF THEY WERE GOING TO *ATTACK* US, THEY'D HAVE DONE IT ALREADY.

YOU DIDN'T KILL ONE OF THEM.

I THINK WE'RE GOING TO GET OUT OF THIS WITHOUT FIRING A *SHOT.*

THAT WOULD BE A FIRST.

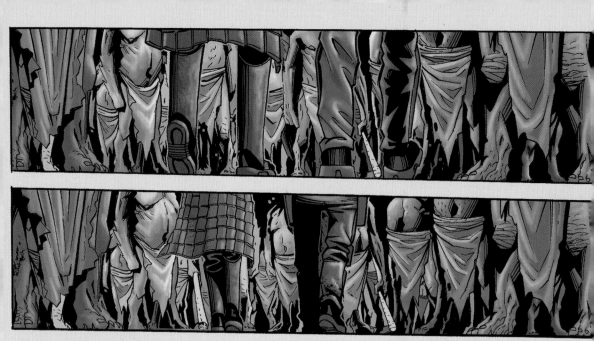

STILL CONFIDENT?

You have brought back that which is ours.

The infant has returned to the mother's womb, where it will remain. Where it will be safe.

We thank you.

WE ONLY DID WHAT WAS RIGHT. THE INFANT NEVER SHOULD HAVE BEEN TAKEN AWAY.

WE'RE SORRY FOR ANY GRIEF YOU HAVE SUFFERED.

We are not unaccustomed to grief. We are a dying people.

Soon we will be gone...

...but now our secrets can die with us.

Go in peace...

...but do not return.

TAKE CARE OF YOURSELF, JANGO...

...UNTIL NEXT TIME.

ZAM...

DADDY!

YOU'RE HOME!

AND VERY GLAD TO BE HERE.

MISS ME?

ALWAYS!

"I THOUGHT I SAW YOU WITH THAT LADY AGAIN. IS SHE A FRIEND OF YOURS?"

"TO TELL YOU THE TRUTH, BOBA...

"...I'M STILL NOT SURE."

"WILL YOU EVER SEE HER AGAIN?"

" I THINK YOU CAN COUNT ON IT."

HE WAS AMONG THE BEST OF US...

...AND WE ARE ALL DIMINISHED BY HIS LOSS.

MASTER YARAEL POOF WAS THE EPITOME OF WHAT ALL JEDI STRIVE TO BE. SO WE GATHER HERE WITHIN THE TEMPLE TO MOURN HIS PASSING, BUT MORE THAN THAT, TO HONOR HIS LIFE.

HE GLADLY GAVE HIS LIFE FOR A CAUSE HE BELIEVED IN.

I'VE SEEN TOO MANY OF THESE, MASTER.

IS THIS WHAT AWAITS ME?

THE PYRE IS THE END FOR WHICH ALL TRUE JEDI ARE DESTINED, ANAKIN SKYWALKER.

YES, THE DEATH OF ANY OF US IS A SAD THING. BUT MASTER POOF IS ONE WITH THE FORCE NOW.

I UNDERSTAND, MASTER WINDU.

"...BUT HEROES DO SOMETIMES COME IN THE MOST UNEXPECTED OF GUISES."

END.

YOU'VE NEVER SEEN
BOUNTY HUNTERS
LIKE THESE...

OTHER TITLES
AVAILABLE FROM TITAN BOOKS

All publications are available through most good bookshops or
direct from our mail–order service at Titan Books. For a free graphic–novels catalogue or to order, telephone 01536 764 646 with your
credit–card details or contact Titan Books Mail Order, AASM Ltd.,
Unit 6, Pipewell Industrial Estate, Desborough, Kettering, Northants.,
NN14 2SW quoting reference SWVP/GN.

FEEL THE FORCE!
ENJOY MORE OF
STAR WARS
EPISODE II: ATTACK OF THE CLONES
WITH THESE OTHER GREAT TITAN PUBLICATIONS:-

STAR WARS MAGAZINE: EPISODE II SOUVENIR EDITION
STAR WARS: EPISODE II ATTACK OF THE CLONES (GRAPHIC NOVEL)
STAR WARS: EPISODE II VILLAINS PACK (GRAPHIC NOVELS)
(FEATURING JANGO FETT AND ZAM WESELL)

STAR WARS: THE OFFICIAL MAGAZINE
STAR WARS: THE OFFICIAL COMIC
STAR WARS: THE OFFICIAL FAN CLUB

CALL 01536 76 46 46 FOR MORE DETAILS
OR EMAIL reader.feedback@titanemail.com

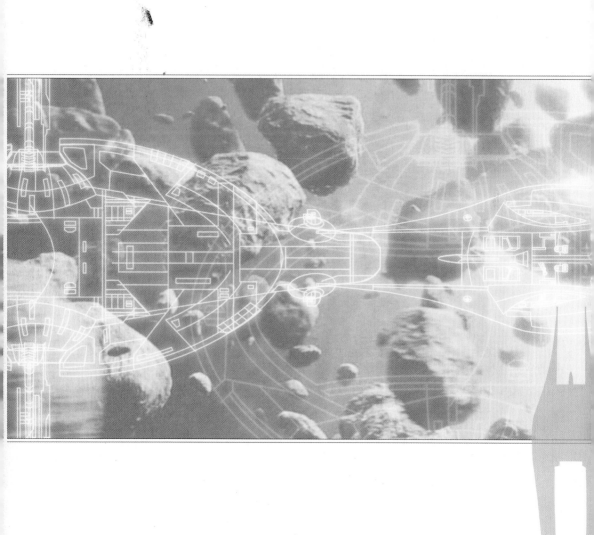